robert jones

beauté occasions
bridal beauty and beyond

written with lisa bower

ISBN 0-9717241-2-1

Hair & make-up: Robert Jones accompanied by Susie Jasper

Representation: Seaminx Artist Management   www.seaminx.com

Producer: Tiffany Mullen, Elaine Moock and Sunni Smyth

Fashion photography: Jeff Stephens

Fashion stylists: Chad Curry, Amy Simmonds (assistant stylist)

Still-life photography: Cindy James

Illustrations: Barbara Camp

Design and Art Direction: The Glassmoyer Group, Inc. New York City

Editor: Lisa Bower

Thank you to Stanley Korshak, Neiman Marcus NorthPark,
Saks Fifth Avenue Galleria Dallas and Myrdith Leon-McCormack New York

Special thanks to Patty Woodrich for her never ending support.

www.simplebeaute.com

This book is dedicated to the people who believed in me, even when I wasn't sure that I believed in myself. Chip, the love of my life. Missy, my best friend. Elaine and Sunni, the rocks that keep me going. Tiffany and Mike, without whom none of this would be possible!

introductiontobeauté

chapter one

There's something exciting about special occasions. Big events like weddings and a special evening out give us the little push we need every now and then to spice up our lives and our looks. Sometimes, the anticipation and excitement leading up to the big event are just as much fun as the event itself. Most women spend hours selecting the perfect dress, jewelry and shoes. And if you're a bride-to-be, you've probably spent months selecting the perfect wedding dress and wardrobe for your entire bridal party.

Most women wouldn't dream of waiting until the last minute to find something to wear to a wedding or a special occasion. Yet that's exactly what many do when it comes to planning their makeup for the same occasion. I encourage every woman to go out and play with color, and find a new look that you really love for your special occasion. The wonderful thing about makeup is that it washes off, so feel free to play! If you don't get the desired look you want, you always have the option to start over.

Keep in mind that while you want to look amazing and beautiful, you also want to look like you, especially if your look will be captured forever in pictures. True beauty comes from the expression in your eyes and the character in your face. It comes from within, and my goal for each of you is to bring out your inner beauty to increase your self-confidence about the way you look. Because while the saying may be trite, it's true: When you look beautiful, you feel beautiful.

In this book, you'll find:

* Makeup tips for brides
* Fantastic makeup looks for special evenings and occasions
* Wedding photo and bridal portrait tips
* Tips on applying makeup for professional portraits and photo shoots

So whether you're a bride or a wedding guest, attending a charity ball or getting a professional portrait done, you'll find plenty of helpful advice and great looks in the following pages to make you look and feel beautiful, inside and out.

bridal beauté

chapter two

I believe that choosing your wedding day makeup look is as important as choosing your gown. Your look will be captured in photos forever so it's important to put on your best face with no mistakes. After all, you are the star, the very center of attention on your wedding day. Why leave your look to chance? This book can help you decide what kind of bride you want to be: a natural beauty, a glamour girl, or a sophisticated bride. With a little planning, practice and advice from me, you and your entire bridal party can look picture perfect on your wedding day.

tiffanymullen

Tiffany's glamorous look is perfect for an evening wedding. I applied a basic three-color eye application in slightly intense shades to help her eyes stand out. False eyelashes help to define her eyes without having to apply heavy eye makeup. The neutral, natural lip color complements her skin tone and allows her eyes to be the focus of the look.

jamiecruise-vrinios

I enhanced Jamie's natural beauty by making the most of her best features. First, I defined her eyes well at the lashline by adding extra lashes. Then I applied a shiny, shimmery eye color to the lids to help her eye color "pop."

missybrumley

Here, I brushed Missy's amazing skin with a warm glow that would look especially luminous in golden afternoon sunlight. I defined her hazel eyes well at the lashline, surrounded them with warm, soft eyeshadows, and glossed her lips to make them pretty and shiny.

maxineallen

Maxine's morning bride look is soft and natural to match the morning light. I subtly defined her

eyes without over-dramatizing them with color, and played up her pretty smile with a rich lipstick shade and a delicate shine.

susanporterglassmoyer

Susan's smile is infectious and truly one of her best features. I evened out her skin tone and used a

great bronzer to give her a natural glow. Next, I subtly defined her eyes and applied a slight shimmer to the lids. Then I layered her lips with color to intensify her smile, and finished with a shiny gloss.

marisol

I rarely recommend a dark lip look for weddings, but Marisol is the exception. Her mouth is the perfect shape for a rich, deep lipstick shade with plenty of gloss to help capture the light and attention. To keep her eye makeup soft and subtle, I applied false eyelashes for slight definition and a light, shimmery shade on her eyelids.

natural vs. trendy

The most important advice I can give you is this: Don't try a new look on the day of your wedding. Stay away from trends and go for a natural look that enhances your best features. Ask yourself this question: If you or your children were to look back on your portrait 15 years from now, would you still think you look pretty? That's a good rule of thumb to follow to decide if the makeup and hair looks you're choosing will stand the test of time.

On your wedding day, you don't want to change your whole look so that people don't recognize you. It is important to look like yourself in the most beautiful way.

perfect timing

chapter three

The time of day you get married will affect your makeup choices. A more natural look for a morning wedding varies greatly from the more dramatic look of an evening ceremony. It's important to consider the time of day when choosing your makeup look. The way the sunlight changes throughout the day can affect the way your makeup appears in photos. It can also affect the type of lighting your photographer will choose when he or she photographs you. Paying attention to these details can help you get the wedding photos of your dreams.

morningbride

If you're planning a morning wedding, your makeup look should appear soft and pretty to match the cool, soft, morning light. Mornings are perfect for the natural girl, because it's the time of day when a bride should wear the least amount of makeup.

* Though matte is always best for photographs, a morning bride can wear a slightly dewy foundation if she chooses. Make sure that your skin is a nice, even tone. For the perfect application that will last all day, see Page 42.
* Go light on the powder so your face retains its natural appearance. Heavy powder can appear artificial, especially in the morning light.
* Do not wear bold lips or eyes for a morning wedding. Choose warmer, soft shades that complement your features. This is the one time you will want to wear less eyeshadow, because the lighting will accentuate any harsh colors or lack of blending. Just make sure to define your eyes really well at the lashline to help them stand out. To learn how to get the most from your mascara for great definition, see Page 48.
* Lip color should always be soft and natural.
* Bridesmaid dresses should be in a soft color and bridesmaids should also wear softer makeup shades.

middaybride

If you're planning a wedding between noon and 3 p.m., be aware that the midday sun can cast shadows on your face, which can make a difference if you're taking outdoor photos. Since natural light is directly above you at this time, you'll want to follow these steps to make sure you are "picture perfect."

* Do not wear dewy foundation or blush with any sheen to it. This is the time when you want to wear the least amount of foundation as possible because it will show the most. A lightweight foundation and a matte powder finish will photograph beautifully.
* Your highlight shade is the most important shadow choice. Use a highlight with shimmer (not frost) to open up the eyes. Due to the midday lighting, if your eye makeup is too dark, your eyes will photograph like dark holes. See Page 47 for the perfect eye shadow application.
* Make sure your midtone and/or contour shade has a matte finish to prevent too much shine.
* A cream blush will absorb into your skin and look more natural at this time, unless you have oily skin.

* If you want more defined eyes, keep your eyeliner close to the lashline to help minimize darkness. Long, beautiful lashes really help define your eyes without depending on heavy eyeliner. To learn how to get the most from your mascara or apply false eyelashes, see Page 48.
* Because the sunlight is growing stronger, every makeup line becomes more visible on your face. Make sure to blend your foundation, blush, eyeshadows and powder very well.

late afternoon bride

The golden light of late afternoon is a photographer's dream when it comes to taking beautiful wedding photos. From 4 p.m. on, you can add a little more drama to your makeup look. The light is growing softer and warmer, so you can wear more eyeshadows and have more shade options.

* If your skin is less than perfect, late afternoon is a great time to get married. The light is softer and more forgiving. Be sure to use a matte powder for best results in photographs.

* Your photographer may decide to use a flash when taking pictures late in the day which can make you appear "washed out." To prevent this I suggest that you contour your face and add a warm glow with bronzing powder. To learn how to contour or "sculpt" your face, see Page 86.

* A shimmery (not frosted) eye is beautiful for this time of day because it photographs well in all lighting. Just make sure that your midtone and/or contour shade is matte.

* Want to add a little more glamour? Try false eyelashes. This is the perfect time of day for this beauty trick and it really helps define your eyes better than anything else. Turn to Page 48 to find out how to apply them.

* Late afternoon brides get the green light to wear a richer lip color and a blush with shimmer, because the soft light will allow it.

evening bride

If you love to glam it up, an evening wedding allows you to go for a more dramatic makeup look. You can play with color and wear more makeup at night than at any other time of day.

* Everything should be more defined, from your lips to your eyes to your cheekbones, because all photos will be taken with a flash which can wash you out a bit. Just make sure to blend well.

* If you have less than perfect skin, this is the best time for you, because you can wear more foundation and powder and still look natural.

* Because all of your photographs will be taken with a flash, make sure to bronze generously to give your skin a glow. To find out how to highlight and contour your face for photographs and prevent yourself from looking washed out, see Page 86.

* Shimmery eyeshadows will photograph well for evening, but absolutely no frosted shadows for this time of night -- or any time for brides! A shimmery shadow always looks soft and pretty. Just make sure to wear at least one matte eyeshadow to prevent your eyes from looking too shiny.

* False eyelashes are a must for a nighttime wedding because they help define the eyes really well during this time of day. Turn to Page 48 to find out how to apply them.

* Try a sultry, smoky eye for a sophisticated look. See Page 69 on how to apply. Just make sure to wear a soft lip color if you're wearing a smoky eye.

* Make sure you have lipstick and powder on at all times. You never know when the camera will flash!

makeup must-haves
chapter four

The key to wearing makeup for your wedding day is to apply it so the color lasts throughout the day and/or evening. It's not a matter of wearing heavier makeup. It's more about choosing the right shades and applying color correctly so it will last and look great under several kinds of lighting, from daylight to twilight to photography lights.

After you've decided on your look and favorite shades to wear, you'll want to pack your makeup bag with the following beauty essentials. This list contains everything you need to help you create a beautiful look and keep you looking radiant throughout your wedding day.

moisturizer

primer

foundation

concealer

loose powder

pressed powder

bronzer

brow pencil

eyeliner

mascara

eye shadows

false eyelashes (optional)

blush

lip pencil

lipstick (2)

lip gloss (2)

brushes

blotting papers

sponges

powder puff

tissues

face

Every bride wants beautiful, flawless skin on her wedding day. To ensure this, you'll want to establish a good skin care routine at least two months before so your skin will appear healthy, smooth and clear. You'll also want to experiment and select your makeup look in advance, practicing it several times before the actual wedding date. You could even use a Polaroid camera to see how your different looks will photograph.

On the day of the wedding, start your look by applying moisturizer and letting it completely dry. I recommend applying a primer next before applying foundation. Primer is an optional makeup step that can do wonders for your skin's appearance. It helps your foundation go on more evenly and makes it last longer. Next, use concealer to cover up any of nature's imperfections, then apply a foundation shade as close to your skin tone as possible. Blot any excess foundation with a tissue to help it last longer.

Because photography can "wash out" the skin, you may want to apply a self-tanning lotion to your face and body a few weeks before the wedding.

Here is the best way to achieve smooth, even coverage when applying self-tanning lotion:
1. Exfoliate well.
2. Moisturize your skin to even out its porosity.
3. For the body: Mix 2 parts self-tanner with 1 part moisturizer and slowly build your color over time to make it appear more natural.
4. For the face: Mix equal parts self-tanning lotion with moisturizer to dilute it slightly, and apply it to your face over a period of days. If you are very fair, you might want to mix 2 parts moisturizer with 1 part self-tanning lotion to make it even more subtle. I recommend doing this gradually over a period of time instead of in one application, so your skin will get a slow build-up of color and appear more natural.

Bronzing powder is also a good choice. It can add warmth to your skin and give you a healthy, happy glow in your photographs. Finally, add a generous dusting of loose powder to your face to set your foundation for the day, help it last longer, and give your skin a smooth, even appearance. Make sure your pressed powder compact isn't far away at the wedding and reception for touch-ups. Well-powdered, matte skin photographs much better than shiny or dewy skin. It's also a good idea to blot your skin with blotting papers or a tissue, before reapplying your powder.

eyes

Your eyes always express your joy and happiness, especially on your wedding day. Because photography is an integral part of the day, it's important that your eye makeup accentuates – not dominates – your eyes. Depending on the time of day and the lighting, your eyes can photograph like two dark holes if your eye makeup is too strong. I recommend staying away from dark or unnatural eyeshadows such as blue or green, and applying a shimmer shadow in natural shades such as ivory, taupe, beige or brown to bring out the color and sparkle in your eyes. Just make sure to always choose shades that enhance your eye color.

To help your eyeshadow last longer, apply concealer and loose powder on your eyelids before applying. This will help absorb any excess oils and help your eyeshadows blend better. Or, you can apply an eye primer that is designed to keep the oils in your eyelids from mixing with the eyeshadows. You'll still want to follow the primer with concealer and loose powder to help the eyeshadows blend beautifully.

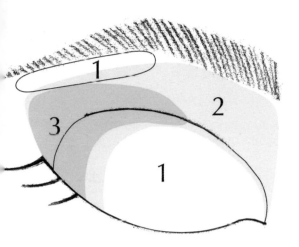

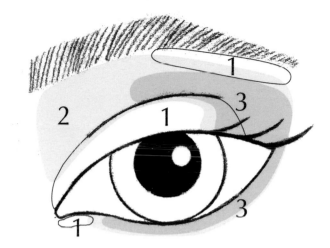

basic eye color application

Eyeshadow is a great way to make the color of your eyes stand out and help define your eyes. To help you apply your shadows properly, follow the steps below for a simple, basic application that will shape your eyelids and make you look absolutely beautiful on your special day.

It takes three shades of eyeshadow to shape the eye: a highlight, midtone and contour shade. While there are thousands of shades to choose from, I recommend using this basic three-shade application technique for best results in shades that complement and enhance your eye color. Application (see diagram):

1. Highlight shade: Apply across the browbone and the lid.
2. Midtone shade: Start from the outside corner of the eyelid so that area will receive the most color. Gently move your brush across the crease into the inside corner of the eyelid.

3. Contour shade: Apply across your upper lashline from the outside corner, inward. Then bring the color up into the outer portion of the crease and blend it inward about 1/3 of the way, layering it on top of your midtone shade. Sweep color underneath the lower lashline for a soft, blended look.

lashes

Your wedding day is definitely the time to define your eyes. I like using false eyelashes to define the eyes at the lashline instead of depending on heavy eyeliner. Here is the easiest way to apply false eyelashes that look natural:

1. Curl your natural eyelashes.
2. Lay a mirror on the table and look down.
3. Draw a thin line across your upper eyelid with an eyeliner pencil. This helps you know where to place the lash and helps conceal the lash band.
4. Trim the outside end of your false eyelashes to fit the width of your eyelid.
5. Apply eyelash glue to the false eyelashes, allow the glue to dry for a minute so that it will get tacky, then place false eyelash right on top of the eyeliner.
6. Apply one coat of mascara to blend your natural lashes with the false ones.

Don't want to wear false eyelashes? Mascara is everyone's favorite way to add definition to the eyes. I recommend applying several coats of mascara to define and open your eyes. If you are concerned about getting teary-eyed during the ceremony or reception, finish with a coat of waterproof mascara. This combination is easier to remove than straight waterproof.

Here's the best way to apply several coats of mascara to "build" lashes that last:

1. Curl your eyelashes with a crimp-style eyelash curler because it opens up the eyes and makes them appear larger and more youthful.
2. If using lengthening or thickening mascara, pull the mascara wand out of the tube and wipe the brush against the opening of the tube to remove any excess.
3. Apply the small amount that is left on the brush to your eyelashes.
4. Let each coat of mascara dry between each application.

For thicker lashes: Hold your mascara wand in a horizontal position. Start at the base of the lashes and move it from side to side as you work your way up to the end of your lashes. This makes the mascara particles attach to the sides of your lashes, making them appear thicker.

For longer lashes: Hold your mascara wand in a vertical position. Starting at the base of the lashline, pull the wand up and out to the end of your lashes. The particles will attach to the ends of your lashes, making them appear longer. If you want both thicker and longer lashes, apply thin coats of mascara allowing each coat to dry completely.

It's important to choose the correct formula of mascara for your desired effect. If you want to just define your eyelashes, use a defining formula. If you want to thicken and lengthen your lashes, choose a formula that will build.

cheeks

Want to be a rosy-cheeked, blushing bride? Here's an easy way to layer your cheek color and make it last from the ceremony to the reception, photo after photo:

1. After applying your foundation, apply a cream blush to the apples of your cheeks and cheekbones.
2. Dust your face with loose or pressed powder.
3. Apply a powder blush (similar in color to the cream blush) to the apples of your cheeks and cheekbones.

Again, finishing with a dusting of bronzing powder can keep your skin looking warm and glowing throughout your wedding day.

lips

You want to give your lip color stay-ability so your smile looks beautiful all day. This is a good time to buy two of your favorite lipstick and lip gloss – one to keep in your makeup bag and one to stash in the groom's pocket for quick lip fixes and instant pretty smiles.

A great way to make sure your lip color stays put is to first conceal the entire lip area. Line the outer edges of the lips with lip liner, then fill in the entire lip area with liner. Next, apply a soft, pretty lip color that looks natural yet still defines the lips. Then, take a tissue and gently blot your lips, then reapply your lip color. Layering color like this will increase the amount of pigment that is deposited on your lips. Finish with a dot of lip gloss in the center of the lips to attract light and highlight your smile for photographs. If you only want to wear lip gloss, make sure to line your entire lip area with pencil so the gloss will last longer.

I usually discourage brides from wearing a dark lip color on their wedding day. It doesn't photograph as well as softer, more natural shades. The only time I'm okay with a dark lip color is if the bride wears it daily and it is part of her everyday look. If you choose to wear a dark lip, remember you must wear a soft eye so the two features don't compete with each other.

light

shimmer flesh

matte taupe

shimmer golden brown

soft coral

glossy coral

natural

medium

shimmer rose

matte dark taupe

matte dark brown

soft rose

glossy nude

dark flesh

colorsuggestions

Here are three basic color palettes to help you create a beautiful bridal look. Based on your skin tone, choose the palette that is right for you.

dark

matte sand

matte caramel

matte charcoal

soft berry

glossy berry

dark chocolate

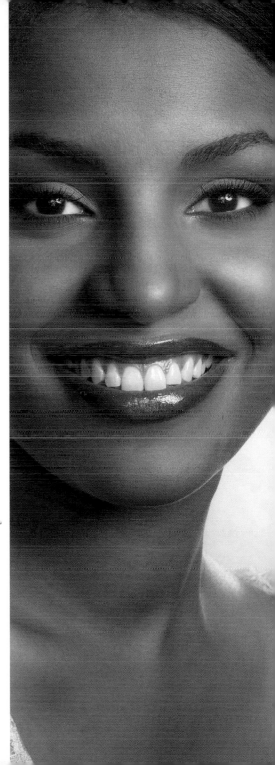

bridesmaids

These days, makeup for the bridal party can be customized to suit each individual bridesmaid. The only thing that should match is the intensity of the looks. For example, you don't want one bridesmaid wearing a dark lip look and another wearing a very pale lip look. You can let each girl individualize her makeup with colors that are the most flattering to her so she can look and feel her prettiest, just like the bride.

Finally, a bridesmaid's makeup should never be more intense than the bride's makeup. The bride should always be the focus of the event. Keep in mind that it is the bride's day, and the bridesmaids are playing a supporting role.

picture perfect

chapter five

When you're considering your makeup look for wedding photos or your bridal portrait, remember that it's all about making your best features stand out in the photo. You want to define your features better – not cover everything up with heavier makeup. Here are a few tips to follow that can help you create beautiful wedding photos and bridal portraits.

* If you're posing for a bridal portrait in a studio, you can wear more makeup than at a morning or midday wedding because you don't have the different lighting factors to consider. If you are posing outside, you'll want to review the tips in Chapter 3 on natural lighting and how it can affect your look during the different times of day.
* Make sure to warm up your skin by bronzing your face. To review tips on how to sculpt the face using bronzing powder, turn to Page 86.
* Blush adds life to the face. You may choose to wear a shade that's more colorful for your portrait than on your wedding day.
* Make sure your lips are well defined for your portrait.

✳ False eyelashes can make a beautiful difference and are the best way to define your eyes for your bridal portrait and on your wedding day. See Page 48 for application tips.

✳ If you want to wear foundation and powder with a bit of sheen to it, you may do so for your portrait if it's in a studio – but not for your wedding day (due to the different lighting).

✳ You can wear matte or shimmer eyeshadows for your portrait and your wedding day, but never frosted shadows. They look too artificial and do not photograph well. Remember, this picture is forever.

✳ Turn to Page 88 for more professional photography and makeup tips.

girls' nightout

chapter six

Nighttime is the right time to add drama and glamour to your look. Whether you're going to a special evening function or to a nightclub, you have more freedom to express yourself and be a little more daring with your makeup. Because the lighting is usually darker, you can wear more intense shades on your eyes and lips. And you don't have to apply your makeup to last all day – only for a few hours. First consider the event or occasion – is it elegant and sophisticated or more fun and wild? Then use your creativity and the following application techniques to stir up a little nighttime magic.

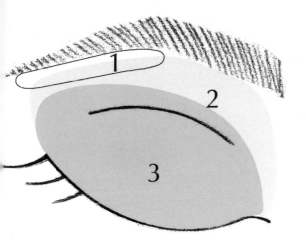

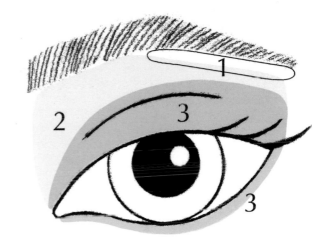

smokyeyelook

Soft, smoky eyes look gorgeous against glowing, luminous skin and perfectly pouting lips. It's just the thing to wear when you want a sexy, sultry look for evening.

Application (see diagram):

1. Highlight shade: Apply to browbone only.
2. Midtone shade: Start at the base of your upper lashline and bring the color up and over your entire lid – all the way up to your browbone.
3. Contour shade: Again, start at the base of your lashline, layer the color over your midtone all the way across your lid and up into the crease. Now sweep the contour color underneath the lower lashline as well. You'll create a light-to-dark effect with the three eyeshadows, with the darkest shade applied closest to the lashline and fading as you go toward the brow.
4. Remember with a smoky eye, it's best to wear a softer lip. Lip gloss really looks perfect with this eye look.

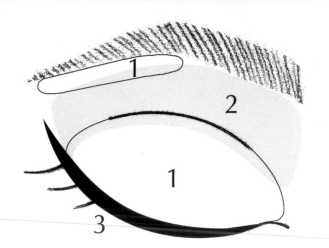

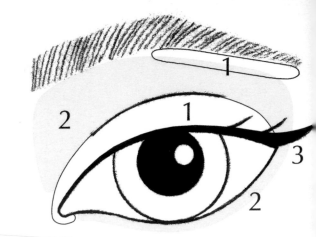

audreyhepburnlook

For fans of *Breakfast at Tiffany's*, this look's for you. Try this cat-eyed look when you want to capture all the attention in the room. It's drama-plus, and guaranteed to bring you long gazes. If you want to increase the drama, wear a rich, deep, luscious lip color and lip liner.
Application (see diagram):

1. Highlight shade: Apply to the browbone and the lid.
2. Midtone shade: Starting in the crease, apply your midtone color from the outer to the inner corner of the eye. Sweep the same color underneath the lower lashline for definition.
3. Eyeliner: Take an eyeliner pencil and line the upper eyelid first. Then follow the line with liquid eyeliner, starting at the inside corner of the eye and kicking it upward at the outer corner. Make sure the line increases from thin to thick as you go toward the outer corner.

4. Highlight the inside corner underneath the lower lashline for added drama.
5. To really finish this look, apply false eyelashes. See Page 48 for easy application steps.

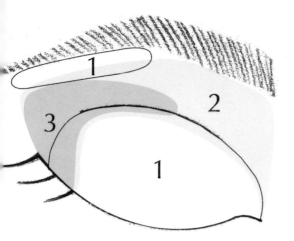

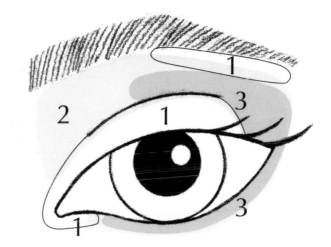

sparklingeyelook

Put a twinkle in your eye and a smile on your face. This look reflects the excitement you feel when you're going out on the town. The key is to wear a sparkly, glittery eyeshadow and keep the shine to your eyes only. Frosted lips and a sparkly blush or face powder can overwhelm you and diminish the sparkle you applied to your eyes. Application (see diagram:)

1. Highlight shade: Apply a sparkly highlight shade to your browbone and lid.
2. Midtone shade: Starting from the outside corner of the crease, sweep the color across to the inside corner of your eye. Make sure this shade is matte.
3. Contour shade: Sweep the color along the upper lashline and into the crease, layering it on top of your midtone shade. Apply underneath the eye all along the lower lashline.
4. Highlight shade: Make sure to highlight the "V" on the inside corner of the eye.

pamshaw

Pam's look is pure glamour. I gave her a slightly smoky eye and added false eyelashes to make her eyes really stand out. Then I bronzed her skin for a pretty glow and finished with a soft lip color and lots of shine to show off her smile.

karenpiro

Karen's quiet, sophisticated look starts with a few extra coats of mascara and a well-defined lashline to make her pretty eyes stand out. I smudged the color at the lashline to keep it soft and natural looking. Finally, I gave her skin a warm, even glow that looks beautiful in the evening light.

annbrown

To transition Ann's look from day to evening, I applied liquid eyeliner in an Audrey-esque style to

define her warm, brown eyes. I played up her beautiful smile by intensifying her lip color and finishing with a gorgeous gloss for added shine. Her dramatic look is perfect for evening, without making her appear overly made-up.

stacyjames

I surrounded Stacy's eyes with warm earth tones to make her amazing eye color stand out. A few

extra coats of mascara make her eyes her most beautiful feature. I accented her pretty cheekbones with color and gave her mouth just a hint of color so it doesn't compete with her eyes.

daytonight

There are times when you have an after-five occasion straight after work. There's no need to rush home and start over. You can transition beautifully from the office to an evening event with these simple steps. Just make sure to pack a few key cosmetics in your makeup bag that day: a more intense or glossier lip color, dark brown or black eyeliner and black mascara. Here are a few options to help you change your look:

✳ Start by adding more mascara to define and lengthen your eyelashes. A few extra layers will definitely pump up your lashes. Make sure to let each coat dry completely in between.

✳ Darken your eye look with eyeliner. Apply it all around the eyes, then take a sponge tip to smudge it out for a smoky effect. With this look your lips need to be much more subtle because of the darker eye. Finish with a shiny, glossy lip color.

✳ Kick your lip color up a notch and apply a more intense shade to define your lips. To really intensify the color, use a matching or slightly darker lip liner over the entire lip area to make your lips stand out even more. With an intense lip color, you'll want to keep your eye look subtle.

soniapaez

To give Sonia a more polished look for evening, I just intensified the colors she normally wears during the day. I added more color and shine to her lips, applied an extra coat of mascara and flushed her cheeks with more color. Her pretty look proves that you don't have to wear dark, intense colors to look glamorous for evening.

wandadalby

Wanda has beautiful skin, and I warmed it up for evening with a soft glow. I brightened her lips for impact and gave them plenty of shine. To keep her eye look subtle and pretty, I softly defined her eyes at the lashline and applied her shadow in a sparkling eye application, but used matte shades for a quiet sophistication.

gaylekolsrud

Because Gayle's eyes are such a beautiful, unusual color, I made them the centerpiece of her look. First, I defined her lashline well and added shimmery, neutral shades to her eyelids. A soft shine on her lips emphasizes their pretty shape and gives her a glamorous yet subtle evening look.

professional photographymakeup

chapter seven

If you decide to hire a professional photographer for a special portrait or occasion, here are a few rules to follow to ensure that you appear in your best light and help your true beauty shine through in your photographs.

lighting

Depending on the lighting and the camera's flash, professional photography can sometimes wash you out and make you appear pale. One way to counteract this problem is by wearing a foundation shade that is slightly darker than your actual skin tone. If you choose this solution, make sure to bring the foundation down onto your neck to ensure your skin will match. However, I think this approach looks the most unnatural. The best way to make your skin appear warm and radiant is to sculpt the face using the highlighting and contouring techniques described on the next page. This will always give your face more dimension in a portrait, and help you photograph more beautifully.

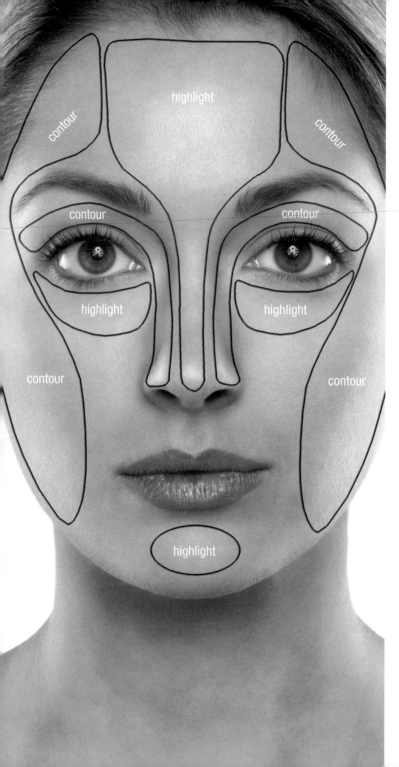

contour

highlight

contour

contour

contour

highlight

highlight

contour

contour

highlight

sculpting techniques

To sculpt the face, you will use three varying depth levels of a foundation shade.

1. The first color should match your skin exactly. It is your true foundation color. Apply this shade all over your face.

2. The second color, your highlight color, should be one level lighter than the first with the same undertone. Apply this shade to the high points of your face including your forehead, under the eyes on top of the cheekbones, and on the tip of your chin. This helps to give your face more dimension by bringing these areas of the face forward.

3. The third shade, your contour color, should be one level darker than your first shade. Apply this shade to the outer areas of your face, including the temples, along your hairline and the sides of your cheeks. This will deepen the skin and help you appear healthier and warmer so you don't look washed out. It also adds dimension and depth to your face while still looking very natural.

To complete your look, you can finish with three shades of powder: one that matches your first foundation shade, one that matches your highlighter shade and a darker or bronzing powder to match your contour shade. This will give you a perfectly sculpted face that will photograph beautifully. Powder is the most important makeup step when doing photography makeup because it eliminates the shine and helps the skin appear smooth and matte – the perfect canvas for beautiful pictures.

blending

Blending also is key when it comes to professional photography makeup. The softer the light, the more perfect your makeup needs to be. The brighter the light, the less perfect your skin has to be. Bright light tends to "blow out the skin" and diminish the fine details. In softer light, the camera can pick up a makeup line along the jaw, neck or eye area, so be sure to blend in your foundation, cheek, lip and eye colors extremely well.

photofacts

* Don't choose shades that are too bold. This is not the time for bright fuchsia lipstick or charcoal eyeshadow. Instead, you should choose shades that are just a few shades darker than your natural skin tone and lip tone. Your goal is to define your features with enough color to see the definition in the photograph, but not so much that you overwhelm and distort your features.
* When choosing eyeshadows for photography, shades with warm undertones enhance every eye color, including brown.
* Warmer cheek colors photograph more beautifully than cool because they make the skin look fresh and glowing.
* Define your lips with a lip pencil for better definition, even if you're just wearing lip gloss.

* Shimmer eyeshadows with just a hint of sheen give eyes a subtle glow when photographed. Always stay away from frosted eyeshadows for your professional portrait. They do not photograph well because they look too artificial and lifeless.
* Make sure at least one of your eyeshadows has a matte finish, especially your midtone shade.
* Brows should be well groomed and defined with brow color.
* Add more definition to your lashes by applying a few extra layers of mascara or by applying false eyelashes. See Page 48 for multiple coat mascara and false eyelash application tips.
* Make sure skin is not too moist or dewy. It will not photograph well. Always lean toward a matte finish for photographs.

lastbutnotleast

chapter eight

After reading this book, I hope you're excited and ready to experiment with new colors to find the perfect look for your wedding or big occasion. These beauty tips are intended to make you feel beautiful and confident on one of the most special days of your life. If you would like to learn more about the basics of everyday beauty, be sure to check out my book, *Simple Beauté*. Available on my Web site at *www.simplebeaute.com*, this book can help you "demystify" the art of makeup and teach you simple techniques for applying foundation, eyeshadow, blush, lipstick and concealer.

I also want to emphasize how important it is to remember that makeup is meant to be beautiful, and beautiful makeup is all about the colors you use and where you place them. Makeup should be used to accentuate and highlight your best features – not to cover up or disguise you. Instead of focusing on your flaws, learn how to focus on your best, most beautiful features. Despite what the magazines show you, there is no such thing as a naturally perfect face. Every face has its own unique and beautiful features, and the sooner you discover and celebrate yours, the happier and more confident you'll be, whether you're walking down the aisle soon, or getting ready for the event of your life.

aboutthe author

Beauty expert Robert Jones is a respected international hair and makeup artist. Formally trained as a painter at the Houston Museum of Fine Arts, he brings an artist's eye to his work, applying the rules of light, undertones and blending to some of the world's most recognizable faces. Robert's work can be found among the fashion pages of *Marie Claire, Allure, In Style, Jane, Elle, Shape, Elegant Bride, Modern Bride* and numerous other fashion catalogs and magazines. He has traveled the world working on magazine shoots and with numerous celebrities, from rock stars to actresses.

He also has had the privilege of working on exciting and lavish celebrity weddings. Robert's commercial clients include Mary Kay Inc., Neiman Marcus, Bergdorf Goodman, Lord and Taylor, Watters and Watters and many others. He is the author of *Simple Beauté*, a beauty handbook designed to help women of all ages define their best features and build their self-esteem and confidence. He splits his time between New York and Dallas, working on a variety of fashion shoots and commercial projects. He also conducts monthly makeup workshops across the country, teaching women how to look and feel their very best.